Deep Snow

Other books by Robert Munsch:

Alligator Baby
Andrew's Loose Tooth
Get Out of Bed!
Ribbon Rescue
We Share Everything!
Mmm, Cookies!
Aaron's Hair
Up, Up, Down
Makeup Mess
Playhouse
More Pies
Zoom!
Smelly Socks
Boo!
Munsch More!
The Sandcastle Contest
I'm So Embarrassed!
Lighthouse: A Story of Remembrance

Deep Snow

by **Robert Munsch**

illustrated by **Michael Martchenko**

Scholastic Canada Ltd.

Toronto New York London Auckland Sydney
Mexico City New Delhi Hong Kong Buenos Aires

Scholastic Canada Ltd.
604 King Street West, Toronto, Ontario M5V 1E1, Canada

Scholastic Inc.
557 Broadway, New York, NY 10012, USA

Scholastic Australia Pty Limited
PO Box 579, Gosford, NSW 2250, Australia

Scholastic New Zealand Limited
Private Bag 94407, Greenmount, Auckland, New Zealand

Scholastic Ltd.
Villiers House, Clarendon Avenue, Leamington Spa,
Warwickshire CV32 5PR, UK

6 5 4 3 2   Printed in Canada   06 07 08 09 10

To Ali and Kate Lucas,
Goose Bay, Newfoundland
— R.M.

Way out in the middle of nowhere, Ali suddenly yelled, "STOP!"

"What's the matter?" said her father.

"I want to jump in the snow," said Ali.

"No," said her sister Kate, "that is deep, deep, deeeeeeeep snow!"

"I still want to jump in it," said Ali.

"This is not a good idea," said Kate.

Ali stood up on the seat, gave her best yell, jumped out as far as she could, landed in the snow and disappeared: WHOOMPH!

All that was left was a hole in the snow.

"She is totally gone," said Kate. "She's at the bottom of a drift."

"Kate," said their father, "jump down that hole and help Ali get out."

"This is also a bad idea," said Kate, but she jumped down the hole anyway: WHOOMPH!

For a long time nothing happened.

Then their father climbed off the snowmobile, crawled over to the hole in the snow and said, "Hey, Ali and Kate! How are you doing down there?"

Ali and Kate said, "Murf bluk bwaaaaaah," because their mouths were full of snow.

Their father said, "Ali and Kate, speak clearly. I can't hear you."

Ali got the snow out of her mouth and yelled, "GET US OUT OF HERE!"

"Don't worry," said their father. He reached down the hole as far as he could, got hold of something and pulled very hard.

Ali yelled, "AAAAHHHHHH! That's my ear!"

So he let go of Ali's ear, reached down the hole, got hold of something else and pulled very hard.

Kate yelled, "AAAAHHHHHH! That's my nose!"

So he let go of Kate's nose, reached down the hole as far as he could, got hold of something else and pulled very hard.

Ali yelled, "AAAAHHHHHH! That's my lip!"

Finally their dad got hold of their ponytails and pulled as hard as he could, and Ali and Kate came flying out of the hole.

"Good," said their dad. "Now we can go."

"No, we can't," said Ali and Kate. "Our boots are still at the bottom of the hole."

"Oh, rats," said their father. He crawled over to the hole and reached down as far as he could. He didn't find their boots, so he reached way, way, way, WAY down and fell into the hole: WHOOMPH!

Only his boots were sticking up out of the snow.

Ali crawled over to the boots and said, "Hey, Dad! How are you doing down there?"

Their father said, "Murf bluk bwaaaaaah," because his mouth was full of snow.

"Speak clearly," said Kate. "We can't understand you."

"Murf bluk bwaaaaaah," said their father, and then he got the snow out of his mouth and yelled, "GET ME OUT OF HERE!"

Ali and Kate took hold of their dad's feet and pulled as hard as they could. Nothing happened.

"This is very bad," said Ali. "Daddy will have to stay there till springtime. How can he fly his jet if he is stuck at the bottom of a hole?"

Then Kate got an idea. She ran over to the snowmobile and got a rope. She tied one end of the rope around their father's foot and tied the other end to the snowmobile. Then Ali and Kate jumped on the snowmobile and went down the trail as fast as they could: VROOOOMM!

Their father came flying up out of the hole and bounced down the trail after the snowmobile yelling,

"Ow ouch! Ow ouch! Ow ouch! STOP! STOP! STOP! STOP!"

So Kate stopped the snowmobile and there was their father, lying in the snow.

"Daddy," said Ali, "You didn't get our boots after all. We're going to have to do it again."

"Right," said their father, "Let's do it again."

He tied a rope to Ali and Kate's feet and dropped them down the hole.

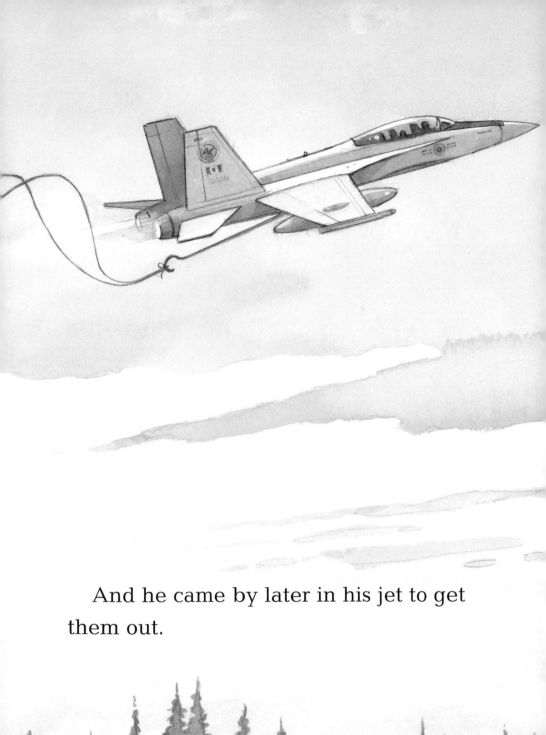

And he came by later in his jet to get them out.

THE WAMPANOAGS

A TRUE BOOK

by

Alice K. Flanagan

Children's Press®
A Division of Grolier Publishing
New York London Hong Kong Sydney
Danbury, Connecticut

Reading Consultant
Linda Cornwell
Learning Resource Consultant
Indiana Department
of Education

A Wampanoag woman
prepares an animal skin.

Visit Children's Press on the Internet at:
http://publishing.grolier.com

Library of Congress Cataloging-in-Publication Data

Flanagan, Alice K.
    The Wampanoags / by Alice K. Flanagan.
        p.   cm. — (A true book)
    Includes index.
    Summary: Presents the cultural, social, and historical achievements of
the Wampanoags.
    ISBN 0-516-20629-X (lib.bdg.)   0-516-26388-9 (pbk.)
        1. Wampanoag Indians—Juvenile literature. [1. Wampanoag Indians.
2. Indians of North America—New England.] I. Title. II. Series.
E99.W2F53   1997
9744'004973—dc21   97-15090
                                                                      CIP
                                                                       AC

Contents

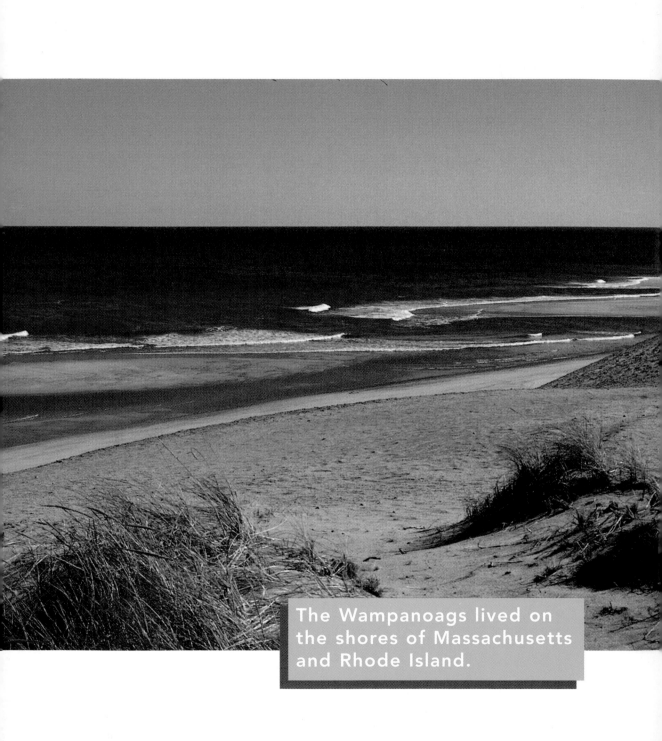

The Wampanoags lived on the shores of Massachusetts and Rhode Island.

Life on the Coast

For many centuries, Wampanoag (wam-puh-NO-ag) Americans and their ancestors have lived along the shores and on the islands of present-day Massachusetts and in the eastern part of what is now Rhode Island. Farming and fishing have been an important part of their lives. Always, they have kept

a special relationship with the ocean, the rivers, the forests, and the wetlands surrounding them.

Today, the Wampanoag territory is much smaller. The people live differently than their ancestors. However, many Wampanoags still live in or near their ancient homeland, and they continue to celebrate their native traditions.

One of their most important traditions is a play that

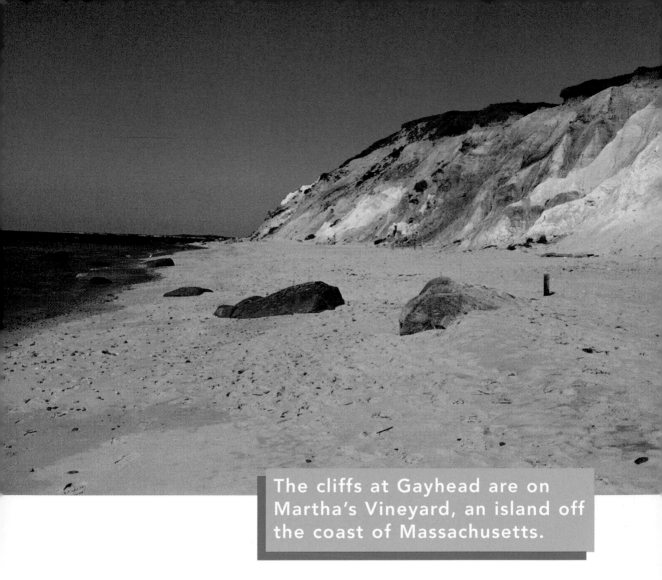

The cliffs at Gayhead are on Martha's Vineyard, an island off the coast of Massachusetts.

recreates the legend of their homeland. According to the legend, Maushop, a giant, created the colorful cliffs of Gay Head, Massachusetts. He was living there when the Wampanoags first settled in the area.

Maushop made friends with the Wampanoags and showed them how to live in peace and harmony. He protected them until the Europeans came. Then he disappeared. But he left smoke from his pipe (the coastal fog) as a reminder of the happy time when he lived among them.

Becoming a Nation

Today, many Wampanoags work and live in cities and towns. More than ten thousand years ago, their ancestors hunted with simple stone tools. Their game included the now-extinct mastodon, the caribou, musk ox, and giant beaver. They also caught fish

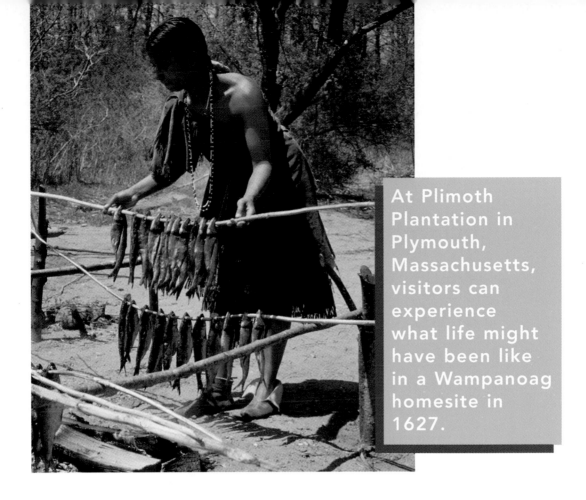

At Plimoth Plantation in Plymouth, Massachusetts, visitors can experience what life might have been like in a Wampanoag homesite in 1627.

and collected roots, seeds, and fruit.

As large animals died out and people learned to farm, families stayed together for several months of the year. They no longer had to move so often to find food. As a result, villages grew larger and tribes were formed. Eventually, several tribes banded together and became known as the Wampanoag. They shared a common territory and way of life.

Today, the tribe is organized into five subtribes, each with its own chief. They are the Mashpee, Gay Head, Herring Pond, Assonet, and Nemasket. Their tribal councils work

Staff members at the Plimoth homesite tend a garden (above) and show how farmers dried pumpkin for winter (right).

together to protect the tribe's land and water rights and to improve the health, housing, and education of their people.

Hunting, Farming, and Fishing

During spring and summer, the Wampanoags lived in coastal farming villages. Only a few family members lived in small, temporary dwellings called *wetus* (WE-toos). Wetus were made of wooden poles covered with woven grass mats or bark.

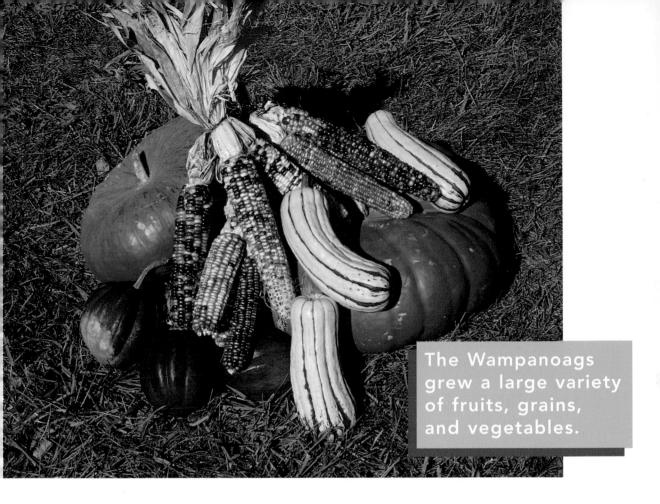

The Wampanoags grew a large variety of fruits, grains, and vegetables.

In spring, everyone helped clear the fields so women could plant seeds. Corn was planted first, followed by beans and a variety of squash.

Usually, the three crops were planted together. Gourds, sunflowers, and tobacco were also grown.

After crops were harvested in the fall, hunting season began. People left their villages and moved inland to permanent winter lodges. The size of the wetu and the number of people sharing it increased. Sometimes, as many as fifty people lived together. Grandparents,

In the winter, the Wampanoags lived in large lodges.

parents, children, aunts, uncles, and friends all shared one house.

In fall and winter, hunters killed deer and bear. They trapped small animals such as

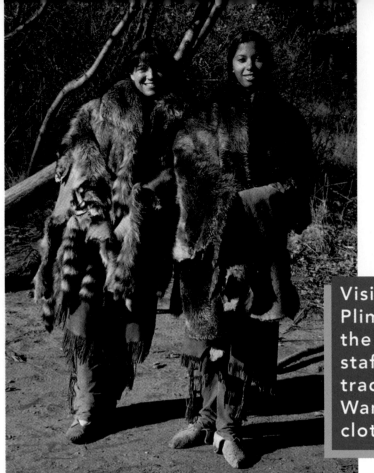

beaver, raccoon, rabbit, and muskrat. From the fur and skin, women made clothing. They dried the meat and stored it. Swans, geese, and ducks also provided food. Turkeys and quail were hunted, too.

From the ocean, rivers, and lakes, people caught fish year-round. In warm weather, the people fished from canoes. In winter, they fished on the ice. There were several ways of fishing—with spears, lines, nets, and weirs (wooden fences built across a river or stream). Along the coast, people gathered oysters, scallops, crabs, and clams. From rivers and

Wampanoags made dugouts, or canoes, called *mishoons*. From mishoons, they fished on lakes and rivers.

lakes, they caught shad, herring, and alewife. Today, some Wampanoags still make their living by fishing.

Sharing Food and Friendship

The Wampanoags are known for their friendliness and generosity. They open their homes to guests and freely share their food with others. This custom may have led to the Thanksgiving holiday we celebrate in the United States today. In the 1620s, the

Friendly Wampanoags welcomed the first English settlers.

Wampanoags shared their thanksgiving harvest with the first English settlers in Massachusetts. They helped the settlers live through the first difficult years in a new land.

The Wampanoags taught the first English settlers important farming skills.

Because of the Wampanoags' help, the Plymouth colony in Massachusetts survived.

Today, the Wampanoag custom of sharing is still practiced. Some families even set extra plates at dinnertime, just in case a surprise guest comes calling.

The Wampanoags have always enjoyed many different traditional foods, which they prepare in several ways. Their main dish is a kind of soup made from corn and beans. To this mixture they add pieces of fish or meat and a variety of squash, roots, and nuts. They boil the soup well until it thickens. Stews are still prepared in much the same

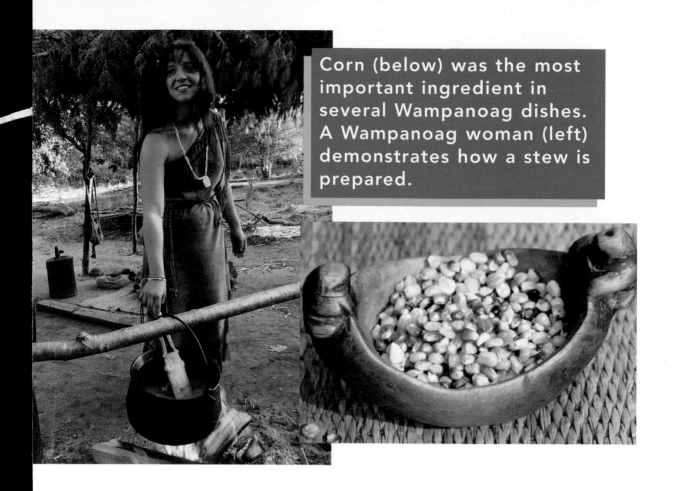

Corn (below) was the most important ingredient in several Wampanoag dishes. A Wampanoag woman (left) demonstrates how a stew is prepared.

way. Today's popular fish boils and clambakes were a common practice in Indian communities of the Northeast a long time ago.

A Thankful Spirit

The Wampanoags have always lived in harmony with nature. They believe that spirits dwell in the forests and waters around them. Even today, many Wampanoags ask the spirits for help and thank them when they bring good things to their lives.

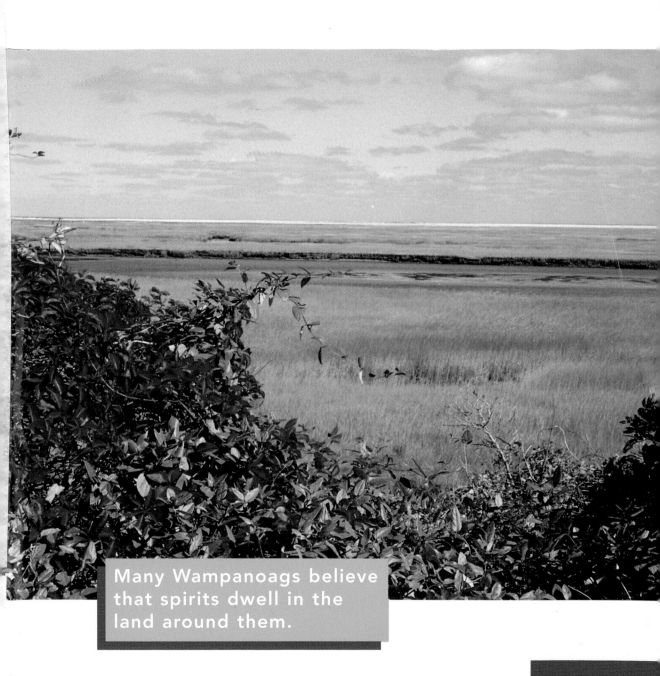

Many Wampanoags believe that spirits dwell in the land around them.

27

In the past, Wampanoags held special celebrations for events, such as a good harvest or hunting season, or the birth of a baby. In Wampanoag communities today, two annual gatherings are held each spring and fall or spring and summer.

In fall, some Wampanoags hold a Green Corn festival in thanksgiving for the harvest. Other Wampanoags have a Cranberry festival to thank the

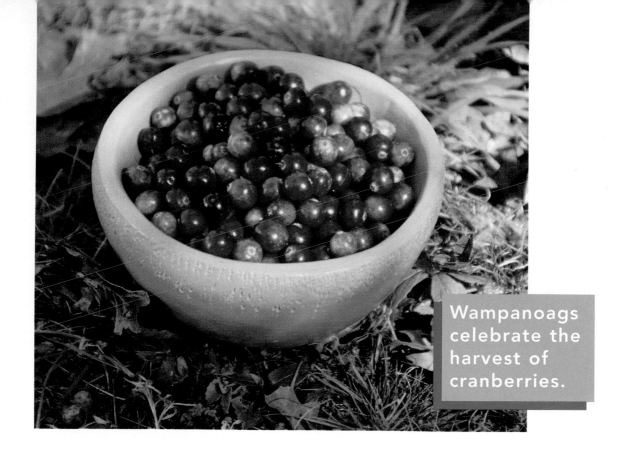

Wampanoags celebrate the harvest of cranberries.

Creator for the first fruits of the cranberry harvest. In May, the Wampanoags hold a New Year's celebration to honor the earth's return to spring after the long winter.

Through prayer gatherings, called unity circles, the Wampanoags strengthen their ties to each other. Anyone can call a unity circle of family, neighbors, and friends. The singing, drumming, and feasting lasts from one to three days.

The Mashpee powwow, which is open to the public each July, is an exciting gathering. Tourists come to watch the singing drummers and

Beaded
Wampanoag
headbands

costumed dancers perform.
Afterward, they can sample
traditional seafoods and buy
native crafts.

Wampanoag

Wampanoag women have long used colorful clay from local riverbanks to make vases, cooking pots, and storage jars. Today's Wampanoag artists also practice this custom.

To the clay, women add finely crushed shells or stones to prevent pots from cracking when they are fired. They wet the clay and

Wampanoags used clay (far left) to make their pots.

Pottery

knead it like bread. Then they shape it by hand or on a potter's wheel. In the past, Wampanoag pottery was shaped like a cone. It was made that way so that it could be pushed down into the soft earth and stand securely on its own.

Today, most women bake their pottery in ovens called kilns. But some make their pottery the traditional way. They heat it in fire pits or bake it in the sun to preserve the bright colors.

Wampanoag pottery

Protecting a Homeland

For most of the 1600s, the Wampanoags lived peacefully with their English neighbors. Massasoit, leader of the Wampanoags, and other chiefs signed a treaty of friendship with the English in 1621. After Massasoit died, his two sons—Wamsutta (also called Alexander) and Metacomet (also called King

As a sign of peace, Massasoit and the English governor smoked a ceremonial pipe (left). During war, Wampanoags fought with clubs (right).

Philip)—tried to honor the promises their father had made. But disagreements over land ownership led to fighting. The Wampanoags could not stand by and watch the English take over their fishing and hunting grounds. They also did not want the English to build houses on land the Wampanoags had cleared for farming.

In 1675, King Philip led several tribes in battles against the English. He was killed the following year, and the fighting known as King Philip's War ended. By then, most of the Indian villages in Rhode Island and Massachusetts had been destroyed. The Wampanoags were scattered. The English

King Philip (left) vowed to drive out the English invaders. The photograph above shows Wampanoag schoolchildren in the late 1800s. They were required to wear American clothes and attend American schools.

sold many of the Indians into slavery and forced others to live on reservations.

Rebuilding a Nation

After many years, some Wampanoags began living and working in non-Indian communities. Some farmed. Most took any jobs they could get as laborers, servants, or sailors on whaling ships. In time, many Wampanoag communities disappeared. So too did many of their traditions.

In 1928, what was left of the Wampanoag nation reorganized, and its people came together to elect new leaders. Today, the highest ranking leader of the Wampanoag nation is still called the Grand Sachem. He is responsible for the people's welfare and appoints a supreme medicine man to handle all spiritual matters. Local governments, led by chiefs and tribal councils, handle the day-to-day operations of the tribe. They are aware of tribal events and have a strong voice in matters affecting the tribe.

A museum at Plimoth Plantation in Plymouth, Massachusetts, employs many Wampanoags to recreate Wampanoag life as it might have been in the 1600s. Here, visitors can see present-day Wampanoags dressed in traditional clothing demonstrating cooking, farming, canoe-building, weaving, basket-making, and pottery-making.

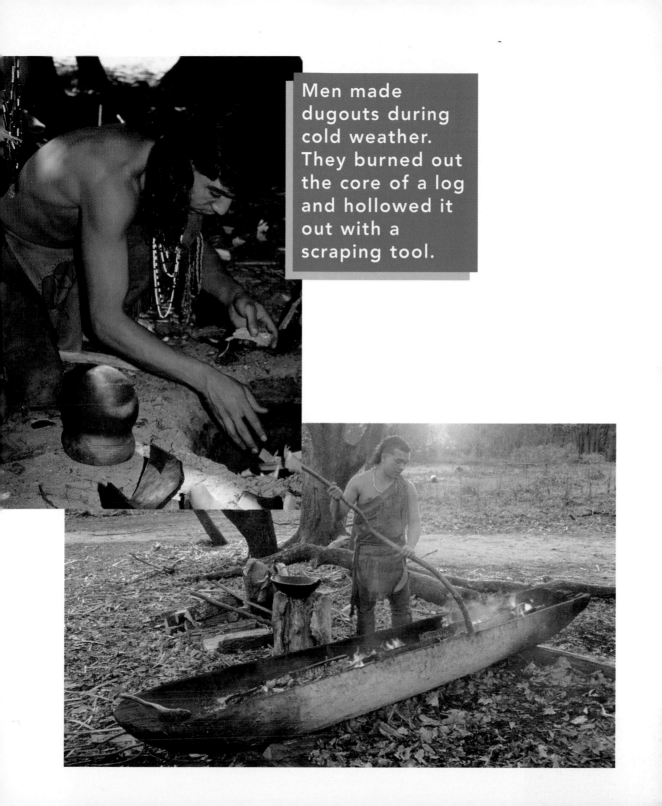

Men made dugouts during cold weather. They burned out the core of a log and hollowed it out with a scraping tool.

Wampanoag Americans

Today, Wampanoag Americans live much like other non-Indian Americans. Their homes, schools, and churches are no different than those in any American city or town. As concerned citizens, they participate in the government. However, to preserve their

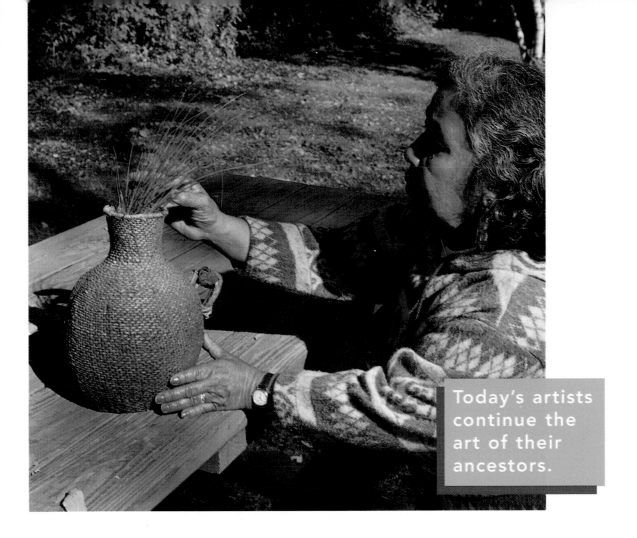

Today's artists continue the art of their ancestors.

native traditions and interests, they remain members of their tribal government and honor their ancient beliefs.

To Find Out More

Here are some additional resources to help you learn more about the Wampanoags:

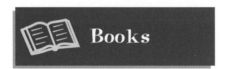 **Books**

Fradin, Dennis. **Massachusetts.** Children's Press, 1994.

Lyback, Johanna R. **Indian Legends.** Tipi Press, 1994.

Miller, Jay. **American Indian Festivals.** Children's Press, 1996.

Miller, Jay. **American Indian Families.** Children's Press, 1996.

First Nations Histories
http://www.dickshovel.com/Compacts.html

This site provides short histories of more than twenty American Indian Tribes.

Mashpee Indian Site
http://www.capecod.net/mashpeecoc/mashpe2.html

This is the homesite to a group of Wampanoags who originally lived on Cape Cod.

Mashpee Wampanoag Indian Artist
http://www.realbodies.com/rpeters/

A contemporary Wampanoag artist uses this site to illustrate Wampanoag approaches to pottery and art.

Native American Nations
http://info.pitt.edu/~lmitten/nations.html

A central site that lists American Indian tribes and links to their sites.

Native American Navigator
http://www.ilt.columbia.edu/k12/naha/nanav.html

A general site that gives hundreds of links to topics on Native Americans.

Native Americans
http://falcon.jmu.edu/~ramseyil/native.htm

A site that lists groups and addresses for those interested in Native Americans.

Plimoth Plantation
P.O. Box 1620
Plymouth, MA 02362
http://media3.com/plymouth/plant.htm

This site provides information about a recreated pilgrim settlement in Massachusetts that includes a Wampanoag village staffed by Wampanoags.

Wampanoag History
http://dickshovel.netgate.net/wampa.html

This site offers a detailed history of the Wampanoag tribe.

Important Words

fire to harden clay pottery with extremely high levels of heat

Grand Sachem leader of the Wampanoags

Green Corn Festival celebration held at the end of the harvest

harvest to gather crops or fruits when they are fully grown

reservation area of land where American Indians were forced to live

unity circle a group of family and friends that is called together for prayer and ceremonies

weir a fence set in a river or stream to trap fish

wetu dwelling made from wooden poles covered with grass or bark

Index

Meet the Author

Alice Flanagan thinks of the world as an open book filled with living stories. As an author, she thinks of herself as an observer—one who watches the stories as they unfold, then carefully writes them down.

Once a teacher, Ms. Flanagan taught Native American children in South Dakota and New Mexico. She feels blessed by the wonderful gifts they shared. Now, through her writing, she tries to pass these gifts on to others. In the True Book: Native Americans series, Ms. Flanagan is the author of the following titles. *The Eskimo, The Chippewa, The Navajo, The Nez Perce, The Pueblos, The Shawnee, The Sioux, The Tlingit, The Utes, The Wampanoags,* and *The Zunis.* Ms. Flanagan lives with her husband in Chicago, Illinois.